THUNDERBIRDS™

INTERNATIONAL RESCUE ANNUAL
2002

SAM DENHAM

CARLTON
BOOKS

This is a Carlton book

Published by Carlton Books Limited 2001
20 Mortimer Street
London WIN 7RD

Text and design © Carlton Books Limited 2001

TM and © 1965 and 1999. THUNDERBIRDS is a trademark of
Carlton International Media Limited and is used under licence.
THUNDERBIRDS is a Gerry Anderson Production.
Licensed by Carlton International Media Limited.
© 1999. The Carlton logotype device is a trademark of
Carlton International Media Limited.

www.thunderbirdsonline.com

A CIP catalogue record for this book is available from the British Library.

ISBN 1 84222 375 5

Photostory Adaptions and Editorial Consultant: Sam Denham
Project Editor: Lesley Levene
Design: Claire Cooper
Production: Janette Davis

To: All International Rescue Agents

From: Jeff Tracy

Security File Code: International Rescue Annual 2002

MESSAGE STARTS Fellow agents...

Since International Rescue first became operational, we've carried out some incredible missions around the world that have saved countless lives, thanks to Brains's amazing technology and the skills of our rescue team. These achievements would not have been possible without the support of our global network of agents, who have shown total dedication to our cause. But to maintain our organization's efficiency in a constantly changing world, it is vital to keep the network fully updated with the latest information, not only about International Rescue but also about new scientific developments and the dangers the planet faces from ruthless enemy forces. To ensure that this information reaches all agents, I have authorized the release of this new International Rescue videfile. Its contents must of course be closely guarded to prevent endangering our security. **F.A.B.** ...**Jeff Tracy.**

MESSAGE ENDS

CONTENTS

Datafile: **Mission Successful**

Report Filed By: Scott Tracy

Hello there, and welcome back. It's been a really exciting year for everyone at International Rescue. We've been called out to locations all round the world to help all sorts of people. We've decided to remind you of just a few of our most challenging operations, when we had to find ways to rescue ordinary people who had been caught up in extraordinary situations.

SPOKE CITY INFERNO!

When Tom Prescott was driving home from work he picked up a hitchhiker – but soon wished he hadn't, as the hitchhiker was part of the Erdman gang. A bracelet packed with explosives was strapped to his arm and he was told the key to release it was back in his office. He returned there as fast as he could, but although he managed to remove the bracelet, he didn't have time to leave before the building exploded in flames, destroying files on various criminal organizations. The fire service was helpless, but International Rescue was on hand. Virgil and Alan beat their way through the flames to rescue a relieved Prescott.

DISASTER AT ALLINGTON SUSPENSION BRIDGE!

The world watched the Martian Space Probe rocket on its journey to a launch site in England, but disaster struck when the Allington Suspension Bridge collapsed under its weight. The rocket plunged into the river, with two engineers inside, and

the automatic countdown started. The authorities were sure they could get the men out, but all their efforts failed. Luckily, Brains was on hand to call International Rescue, and Gordon and Virgil were able to rescue the engineers with seconds to spare.

CORRIDORS OF FEAR!

Joe Carter, his wife, Blanche, and their young son, Tommy, had planned a day out at the Thompson Tower, but instead found themselves trapped in an inferno when the tower's safety systems failed. As a fire in an underground car park spread to the main building, which then collapsed, they were stuck in a sealed corridor with no hope of escape. Luckily for them, the Tower Controller contacted International Rescue, and Virgil and I raced to the scene. We were able to use new equipment to cut through the fire doors and managed to rescue the Carter family just as the corridor roof collapsed.

NEW YORK CITY TERROR!

As part of a scheme to redevelop Manhattan Island, planners decided to move the Empire State Building on a giant track. Ned Cook was the lucky reporter covering the story – but maybe he wasn't so lucky! An underground river had weakened land beneath the track and the building came crashing down. As it fell, the ground gave way beneath Ned and Joe, his cameraman, and they were buried in an underground cavern. No one could reach them and the cavern was filling with water. To make matters worse, Thunderbird 2 was out of operation, but we managed to rescue Ned and Joe, and what's more, we were all in the audience at Ned's next TV show!

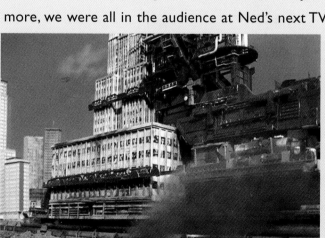

Datafile: The World of 2065

Report Filed By: Brains

Oh, er...hi there. This is Brains reporting. Mr Tracy thought you would be really keen to hear about some of the latest amazing developments that have taken place in the worlds of engineering and technology, so he has asked me if I would tell you all about them.

Thanks to the fantastic work of our scientists, we are now seeing new opportunities open up both on our own planet and in outer space. Never before has it been so easy for ordinary people to travel in safety anywhere in the world, and in space our astronauts are venturing even further afield, to provide vital resources for the human race. So, it is clear that the future will be very, very exciting!

FIREFLASH

Air Terrainean's atomic-powered passenger aircraft, Fireflash is capable of flying at six times the speed of sound. It can carry up to 600 people and flies at a height of 150,000 feet. The cockpit is positioned in the rear tailfin, on top of which is an elevated tailplane which houses six atomic engines. In theory, these engines allow the plane to stay in the air for six months at a time, although the anti-radiation shielding on the reactor obviously requires regular servicing to maintain acceptable levels of safety.

SIDEWINDER

A 500-ton, all-terrain vehicle, built by Universal Engineering Incorporated, the Sidewinder can clear vast areas of jungle with ease to create landing sites for heli-jets and troop-carrying aircraft. After initial operational problems, vertical-thrust hover combines were added to stabilize its progress in difficult conditions.

CRABLOGGER

Built by International Robotics, this forest-clearing machine is a fast and effective way of preparing forested areas for new road-building schemes. The Crablogger makes use of forward-mounted grabs on telescopic arms to cut down trees and feed them into a pulping machine located at the back. Powered by a Superon-fuelled atomic reactor, it processes the resulting wood pulp and packs it into barrels ready for a number of recycling projects, producing up to sixty barrels every thirty minutes.

SUN PROBE

Relying on a new process which converts sea water to rocket fuel, the Sun Probe rocket has a launch thrust of 20 million pounds which gives it the necessary acceleration to reach solar orbit within a week. Now that we have the technology, there is great enthusiam for sending manned missions to the sun. Teams of scientists are confident that it will be possible to collect particles from solar prominences which might be helpful in our endless quest to find new resources that can be used here on Earth.

ZERO X

Space exploration remains high on the agenda of the International Space Control. It is hoped that the Zero X modular spacecraft will play a central role in the Space Exploration Center's first manned landing on Mars. The craft has five component parts: the main body, two lifting bodies, a specially adapted Martian Exploration Vehicle and a heat-resistant nose cone. If all goes to plan, the Zero X will be launched from Glenn Field, Nevada, with a five-man scientific crew. Their mission also is to locate possible new resources for use by the peoples of Earth.

REPORT FILED BY

BRAINS

"Oh, er...Hi there. This is Brains recording. Like most people, I enjoy a change of scene when I go on vacation, so the idea of discovering lost treasure in an ancient temple, found at the bottom of a lake, seemed a great way to get away from designing the fantastic twenty-first-century Thunderbirds machines. But as it turned out, I was extremely glad to see my creations racing to the rescue."

WHEN TIN-TIN AND I FLEW OUT TO THE MIDDLE EAST WITH VIRGIL IN THUNDERBIRD 2, WE HAD NO IDEA HOW DANGEROUS OUR VACATION WOULD BE.

COMING IN TO LAND NOW. AND REMEMBER, NOBODY MUST KNOW YOU'RE CONNECTED WITH INTERNATIONAL RESCUE.

THUNDERBIRD 2 TOUCHED DOWN.

VIRGIL OPENED THE POD...

IF ANYBODY ASKS, WE FLEW OUT BY CHARTER FLIGHT.

AND SOON TIN-TIN AND I WERE HEADING OFF IN THE SAND TRAIN...

TO RENDEZVOUS WITH PROFESSOR BLAKELY FROM THE INTERNATIONAL MUSEUM OF ARCHAEOLOGY, WHO WAS ON HIS WAY DOWN THE DESERT HIGHWAY.

9

SOMEHOW, ONE OF THE WORLD'S MOST NOTORIOUS VILLAINS HAD LEARNED OF OUR EXPEDITION...

AND HAD MADE PLANS TO STEAL THE TREASURE FOR HIMSELF.

SO WHEN WE ARRIVED AT THE LAKE SHORE...

EVIL EYES WERE OBSERVING US.

EXCELLENT. MY FRIENDS ARE DEAD ON TIME!

AFTER SETTING UP CAMP...

WE WERE SOON ON OUR WAY DOWN TO THE LAKE BED...

AND THE RUINS OF THE ANASTA TEMPLE.

IT WAS MY THEORY THAT THE TREASURE WAS HIDDEN IN ONE OF THE COLUMNS OF THE TEMPLE.

THAT COULD BE THE ONE.

LET'S TAKE A SAMPLE BACK TO THE PROFESSOR.

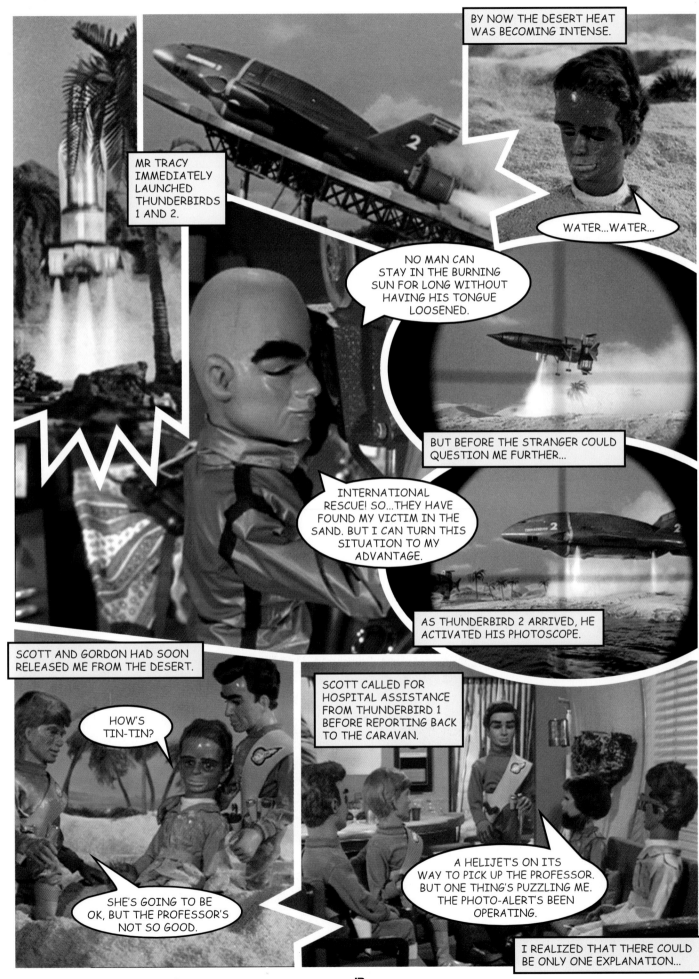

15

BY NOW IT WAS DAYBREAK AND TIN-TIN HAD WOKEN THE BOYS.

THUNDERBIRD 4 WAS IMMEDIATELY SENT TO THE SCENE.

I TRIED TO STOP HIM, BUT HE WOULDN'T LISTEN.

BUT THE ENEMY WAS WAITING.

NOW TO DESTROY INTERNATIONAL RESCUE AND COLLECT THE TREASURE!

A TORPEDO SHOT TOWARDS THUNDERBIRD 4...

AND ONLY JUST MISSED!

GORDON CALLED MOBILE CONTROL.

I'M BEING ATTACKED! THERE'S ANOTHER CRAFT DOWN HERE!

THE CHASE WAS ON!

BUT THE ENEMY CRAFT WAS NO MATCH FOR GORDON.

DIRECT HIT!

MY MOTORS ARE FLOODING!

THE MINI-SUB CRASHED TO THE LAKE BED.

BUT GORDON WASN'T ABLE TO STOP OUR MYSTERIOUS ENEMY MAKING HIS GETAWAY...

BEFORE A MASSIVE EXPLOSION BLEW THE MINI-SUB TO PIECES!

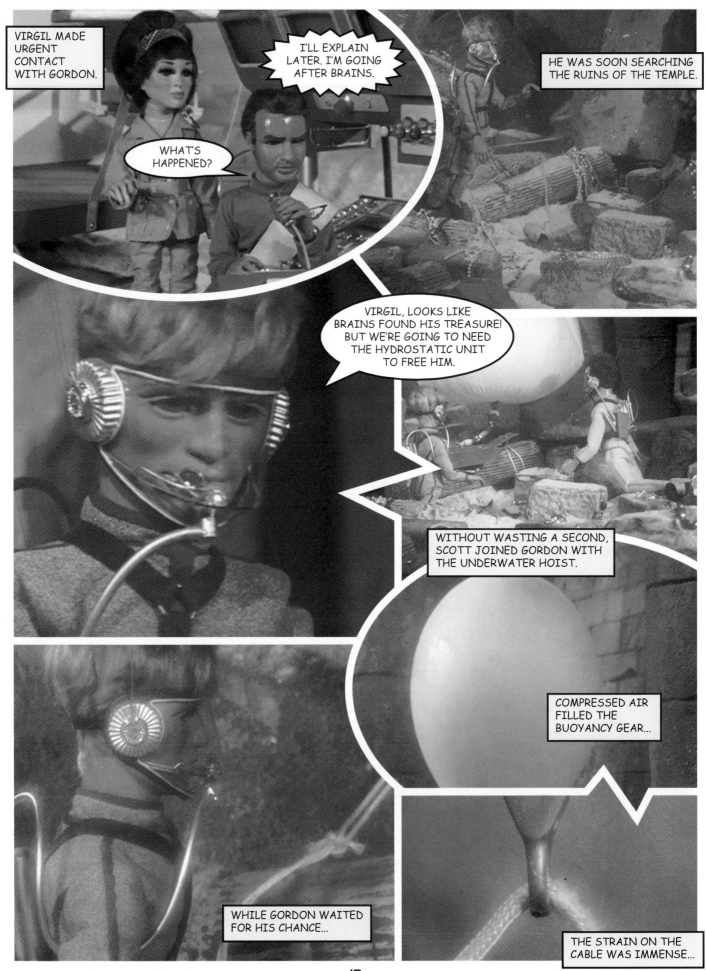

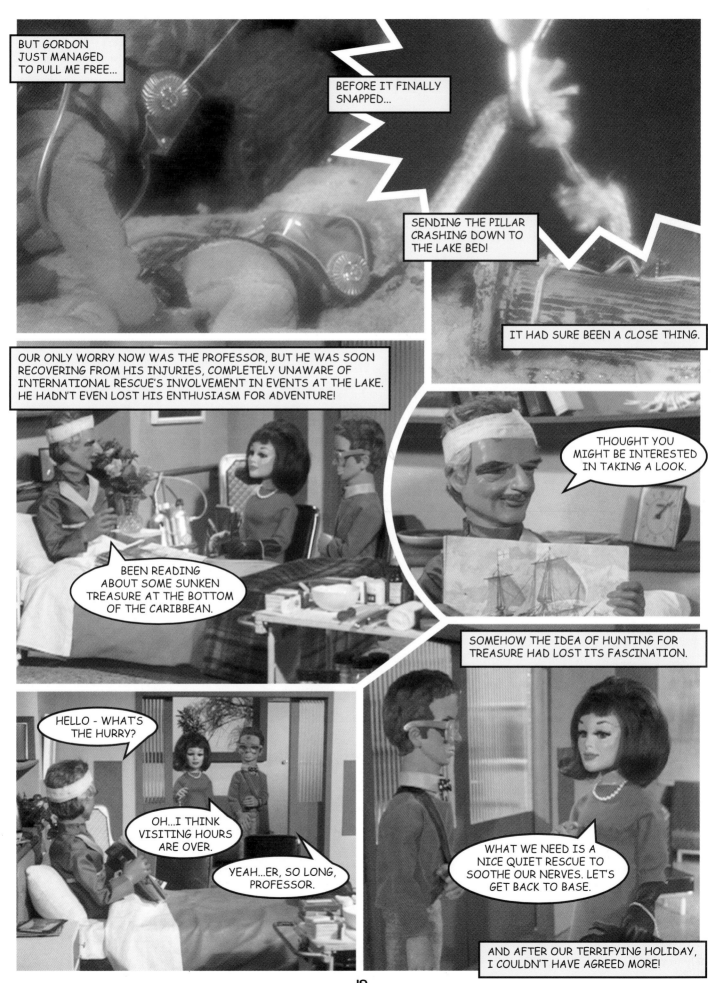

Report Filed By: Jeff Tracy

When I started making plans to form the International Rescue organization, I realized that my first priority would be to find a suitable operations base – a location where all International Rescue's craft could be stationed ready for immediate launch, that would provide space for laboratories and workshops, and that wouldn't attract the attention of the outside world.

After considering remote areas of Canada and mountain ranges in South America, I remembered a location that would be ideal that I'd come across during an Aerospace plane test flight for the World Space Agency. It was remote, honeycombed with caves and would provide the perfect cover for a secret base. After making inquiries, I discovered that the site was for sale and soon the Tracy family had a new home – an island in the Pacific.

With the tireless help of my five sons, and with the inventive genius of Brains to guide us, the task of

THUNDERBIRD 2'S HANGAR, CARVED FROM A VOLCANIC CAVE

TRACY ISLAND

LABORATORY FACILITIES

CONFERENCE ROOM

transforming the barren volcanic outcrop began. Using robot construction vehicles developed by Tracy Engineering, we began building an airstrip and a luxury villa. To the outside world it appeared that I was creating a new home on the island. In reality, the maze of volcanic caves beneath the surface was being enlarged and converted into hangars, workshops and laboratories.

Finally the island was ready for action and, with the activation of the Operative Cover-up Programme,

ready to receive its first unsuspecting visitors. To them it is nothing more than a millionaire's paradise, with all the facilities they might expect: a private airstrip, a swimming pool, games rooms and accommodation for guests. Visitors can even go to the caves on the far side of the island to hunt for water mambas. But all the time, behind the idyllic façade, International Rescue is on constant stand-by, awaiting the request for help that will send us out on another exciting mission.

JEFF TRACY'S CONDOR XL6 JET

TRACY VILLA

Agent Challenge: Sun-spot Alert

Challenge Set By: John Tracy

Hi there! This is John Tracy speaking. Due to increased sun-spot activity that is now affecting large areas of the world, reception of radio transmissions is being disrupted. As a result all messages have been split into red and green colour-coded signals. Can you help us by putting the messages back together by combining the letters in signals 1A, 2B and 3C in the order in which they appear below? Are any of them distress calls?

1 This is Control Tower.

Aircraft crash-landed on roof. Passangers trapped.

2 T_i_ i_ c_r_ _w_ o_ e _a_n_ S_o_e _i_y _o_t_o_.

N_ i_c_d_n_s _o _e_o_t _t _r_s_n_.

3 T_i_ i_ D_s_r_ S_r_e_ T_a_ S_v_n.

_a_e _o_ c_m_l_t_d _o_k _n _h_s _r_a _s _l_n_e_.

CONTROL TOWER

4 This is Control tower

_i_c_a_t _r_s_-l_n_e_ o_ r_o_ P_s_e_g_r t_a_p_d.

B _h_s _s _a_ t_o_n_ c_l_i_g _p_k_ C_t_ c_n_r_l

_o _n_i_e_t_ t_ r_p_r_ a_ p_e_e_t.

DESERT SURVEY TEAM SEVEN

C _h_s _s _e_e_t _u_v_y _e_m _e_e_.

H_v_ n_w _o_p_e_e_ w_r_ i_ t_i_ a_e_ a_ p_a_n_d.

See page 60 for Solutions

SPOKE CITY PATROL CAR

Challenge Set By: Jeff Tracy

This is Jeff Tracy reporting...We've picked up a distress call from a rocket transporter shot down over the Gobi Desert. We have 3 rescue vehicles in range, but have not pinpointed the exact crash site. The pilot has contacted us to describe the route he took before his rocket was shot down.

Can you follow his directions to help us locate him? Mark the crash site with a cross and see which vehicle he is closest to.

VEHICLE A: THUNDERBIRD 2

The pilot took off from point **X** and flew 500 miles north before turning east at an oasis and flying 1,000 miles. From here he went north for a further 500 miles, then headed 600 miles west. At this point he turned to the north again and proceeded for 500 miles and then went west for another 400 miles, at which point he was shot down.

VEHICLE B: THUNDERBIRD I

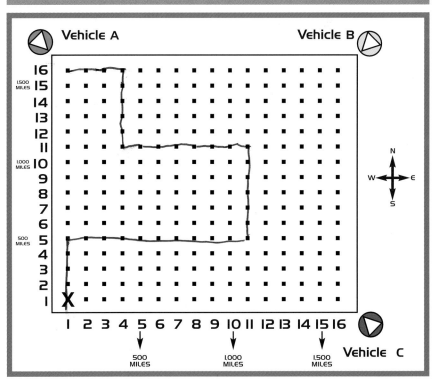

VEHICLE C: CONDOR XL6

See page 60 for Solutions

Datafile: Designed for Danger

Report Filed By: Virgil Tracy

Hi there! This is Virgil Tracy reporting. When we first began turning the dream of International Rescue into a reality, one of our top priorities was to create the specialized equipment needed to carry out rescues when all other means had failed. After designing the main Thunderbird craft, Brains immediately turned his attention to this vital task. By using new and untested technology in combination with readily available components, he completed the job in record time and details of some of these incredible designs can now be released. This information can be used by field agents to provide us with vital mission advice when reporting emergencies.

THE MOLE

At 30 tons, the Mole is one of the larger pod vehicles. A jet-propelled boring machine, it can cut through metal at a speed of 15 m.p.h. Equipped with a 3D thermal-imaging system, it can locate a trapped person with complete accuracy.

THE FIREFLY

Combining fire-fighting, site-clearance and demolition roles, the Firefly is one of International Rescue's main pod vehicles. It has a cahelium extract X-built shield that performs a dual role as dozer blade and high-impact protective blast shield.

THE DOMO

The Demolition and Object Moving Operator is a tracked restraining vehicle that is fitted with three revolutionary artificial-gravity-field suction pods on the end of jointed arms. Used to clear disaster zones of heavy objects and secure dangerous buildings, it can lift up to 50 tons and support even greater weights.

RECOVERY VEHICLES

Used to drag heavy metal objects out of danger, Recovery Vehicles have magnetic clamps that can be fired up to 300 feet and powerful winches that then haul the objects in.

ELEVATOR CARS

The twelve-wheeled, high-speed Elevator Cars were designed to be used at airports to provide mobile landing facilities for planes with disabled landing gear.

EXCAVATOR

A high-powered rock-crushing machine, the Excavator is used to clear rough ground and is particularly effective in areas that are troubled by landslides.

MONOBRAKE

A tracked search and recovery vehicle, the Monobrake was designed for use on monorail lines. When required, a front-mounted telescopic arm is attached to the overhead monorail to increase speed.

TRANSMITTER TRUCK

Based on a heavy-duty commercial vehicle, the Transmitter Truck uses a Jodrell Six multi-use dish to transmit radio safety and tractor beams, plus communications signals and computer data, to and from areas normally out of range.

FIRE TRUCK

Another formerly commercial vehicle adapted for use by International Rescue, the Fire Truck has been modified to fight any kind of fire. As well as having powerful water pumps and foam-storage tanks, it can also snuff out fires or create firebreaks by the use of nitro-glycerine shells.

THE MOBILE CRANE

This is a six-wheeled truck equipped with a telescopic arm that can raise a maintenance platform up to heights of around 50 feet.

REPORT FILED BY **LADY PENELOPE**

"This is London agent Lady Penelope reporting. When Jeff Tracy asked me to leave the Federal Agents Bureau and join the International Rescue team, he knew my special agent skills would be invaluable to his organization. This mission in the South of France proved he was right."

MONTE CARLO AT NIGHT –

THE PERFECT LOCATION FOR A SECRET RENDEZVOUS.

BUT SUDDENLY...

SABOTAGE! THE COURIER'S YACHT SANK TO THE BOTTOM OF THE BAY.

THE CONTACT – BRITISH AGENT BONDSON.

THERE SHE IS! MOVE IN AND TIE UP ALONGSIDE.

NO SIGN OF BLACKER. I'D BETTER GET DOWN THERE.

BUT WOULD THE WRECK SURRENDER ITS SECRETS?

WHILE PARKER DROVE ME ALONG THE COAST ROAD TO MONTE CARLO IN FAB 1...

BONDSON WAS WARY.

AT MIDNIGHT YOU WILL DRIVE TO THE FOREST OF DIGNE. YOU WILL COME TO A CLEARING THREE KILOMETRES WITHIN THE PERIMETER. THERE YOU WILL WAIT.

HOW DO I KNOW I CAN TRUST YOU?

I GAVE BONDSON HIS INSTRUCTIONS USING A DISGUISED VOICE, BY SOUND-ONLY VIDECALL -

YOU DON'T. IT WAS YOU WHO ASKED US FOR HELP, REMEMBER?

SO, AT MIDNIGHT, BONDSON PULLED INTO THE CLEARING...

DON'T MAKE A MOVE OR IT WILL BE YOUR LAST. NOW TELL ME WHY YOU NEED INTERNATIONAL RESCUE.

AND I MADE CONTACT.

A FELLOW AGENT WAS ABOUT TO DELIVER PLANS FOR A NUCLEAR DEVICE - PLANS THAT WOULD PUT THE WHOLE WORLD IN DANGER IF THEY FELL INTO THE WRONG HANDS.

AND THAT IS PRECISELY WHAT HAPPENED?

YES.

BONDSON RECOUNTED THE FATE OF HIS CONTACT AND HIS DISCOVERIES ABOARD THE WRECK OF THE YACHT.

I HAD HEARD ALL I NEEDED.

DO NOTHING. SAY NOTHING. I WILL CONTACT YOU. NOW REMAIN AS YOU ARE FOR TEN MINUTES, THEN RETURN TO YOUR HOTEL.

HE'D BEEN SHOT FIVE TIMES BY A HENRETTA 45 SUPAMATIC.

28

WE WERE SOON ABOARD THE KILLER'S BOAT...

HEADING FOR A BOATHOUSE ON A DESERTED STRETCH OF COAST...

WHERE MY FATE WAS REVEALED.

SO WE DETONATE THIS LITTLE BOX OF TRICKS WHEN A PATROL BOAT ENTERS THE BAY. THE PATROL BOAT COMES TO INVESTIGATE THE EXPLOSION... YOU DIE... AND WE ESCAPE.

OUR SUB IS STUCK ON THE BOTTOM OF THE SEA BED, BECAUSE IF WE MOVE, PATROL BOATS IN THE AREA WILL PICK US UP ON THEIR SONAR.

NOW I KNEW THEIR PLAN, I HAD TO CONTACT JEFF.

THE KILLER DIDN'T REALIZE MY COMPACT WAS A SECRET RADIO TRANSMITTER.

MY FACE IS SUCH A MESS. AS A LAST REQUEST, WILL YOU LET ME FIX IT?

IT'S LADY PENELOPE!

EMERGENCY CODE!

I'LL TAKE IT AT MY DESK.

USING COSMETIC CODE, I TRIED TO WARN JEFF OF THE DANGER...

BEFORE THE COMPACT WAS KNOCKED FROM MY HAND.

HELD CAPTIVE... BOATHOUSE...BOMB!

THAT'LL DO! YOU'VE PRETTIED YOURSELF UP ENOUGH.

I HOPED THE COMPACT WAS STILL TRANSMITTING WHILE I WAS TIED TO A CHAIR.

JEFF TRIED TAPPING A MESSAGE USING THE AUDIO CODE SIGNAL.

WHAT WAS THAT?

IT MUST HAVE BEEN RATS. DO YOU THINK THEY'LL LEAVE THE BOAT BEFORE THE BOMB GOES OFF?

I'M GOING TO TURN UP THE SOUND LEVEL.

LUCKILY, I WAS STILL WITHIN RANGE OF THE COMPACT.

WHAT A SITUATION!

BUT WE KNOW FOR SURE ONE OF THE MURDERERS IS STILL ABOARD.

AND HE'LL BE BOUND TO GIVE HIMSELF TIME TO GET CLEAR.

RIGHT, SCOTT, OFF YOU GO! AND I FIGURE THE KILLERS HAVE A SUBMARINE STANDING BY...

SO WE'LL NEED THUNDERBIRD 4.

ON BOARD THE BOAT I TRIED TO RAISE JEFF...

ARE YOU RECEIVING ME?

BUT IT WAS NO GOOD.

PENNY, CAN YOU GET ANY CLOSER? I CAN'T HEAR YOU.

I STRUGGLED TO GET NEARER...

UNTIL FINALLY...

WHY, PENELOPE... ARE YOU ALL RIGHT?

JEFF, THOSE KILLERS ARE HIDING OUT IN A SUB. THEY'RE GOING TO DETONATE THE BOMB ON THIS BOAT AS SOON AS THE LOCAL PATROL BOAT COMES INTO THE BAY.

ALL RIGHT, PENNY. I'LL TELL SCOTT TO PREPARE HIS SONAR EQUIPMENT.

BUT WOULD THEY GET TO THE BOATHOUSE IN TIME?

34

AS SOON AS SCOTT ARRIVED AT THE DANGER ZONE...

HE LOWERED THE ULTRA-SENSITIVE SONAR EQUIPMENT BRAINS HAD DEVELOPED.

I'M GOING TO COVER THE AREA IN A WIDENING CIRCLE. LET'S HOPE WE HAVE ENOUGH TIME.

VIRGIL CALLED THROUGH FROM THUNDERBIRD 2.

AND THEN...

SUBMARINE LOCATED AT AREA 243, REFERENCE 19, CHART 9!

APPROACHING DANGER ZONE. ABOUT TO LAUNCH THUNDERBIRD 4.

VIRGIL LAUNCHED THUNDERBIRD 4...

AND GORDON WAS SOON DIVING TO THE DEPTHS OF THE BAY.

BUT MEANWHILE, ON THE SUBMARINE...

PATROL BOAT NOW APPROACHING THE BAY.

WOULD GORDON BE IN TIME?

Report Filed By: Lady Penelope

THE CREIGHTON-WARD RANCH AT BONGA-BONGA

When Jeff Tracy asked me to join the International Rescue team, the first words I heard were, "Secrecy is essential!" As he explained his ambitious plan to use fantastic new technology to provide a means of rescue when all hope seemed lost, I could understand his concern.

I soon found that I wasn't the first person he'd approached to help him achieve this dream, and I was amazed to discover he'd already established a global network of agents. Their task: to help set up his organization and run its essential supply and intelligence operations. With friends and contacts in the US Air Force, the World Space Agency and the aerospace industry, Jeff was able to recruit dozens of loyal and trusted helpers.

Through them, International Rescue could obtain vital components, the latest technical information and reports on potential disasters. I was astonished to learn that a very close friend of mine, Sir Jeremy Hodge, had been one of his earliest recruits.

However, Jeff soon realized that he had no one with the special agent skills and the international social contacts that I could offer. During my time

SIR JEREMY HODGE

FAB 2 MOORED OFF THE COAST OF MONTE CARLO

with the Federal Agents Bureau, I'd established the perfect cover as a jet-setting journalist and fashion model. The bureau had already equipped my mansion at Foxleyheath, my Rolls-Royce, FAB 1, and my ocean-going yacht, FAB 2, with the latest special agent gadgets, and thanks to the work I'd carried out for them in the Far East, I also had a base at Bonga-Bonga in the Australian Outback. With the unique additional talents and underworld connections that my chauffeur, Parker, has to offer, I am in an ideal position to advise the agents' network on new ways to improve efficiency.

But even I can sometimes underestimate the resourcefulness, dedication and skill of Jeff's recruits. For example, no one would suspect that a run-down shack in the backwoods of America is in fact an efficient operations base, but with their concealed gas-range monitor system,

JEFF TRACY CONSULTS THE CHART LOCATING HIS AGENTS

supercharged Model T Ford and exploding cans of beans, Jeremiah and Ma Tuttle are more than a match for any enemy agent!

I hope it won't be too long before I meet the other members of International Rescue's agents' network, but if they are all as resourceful as the Tuttles, I have a feeling the security of the organization is assured.

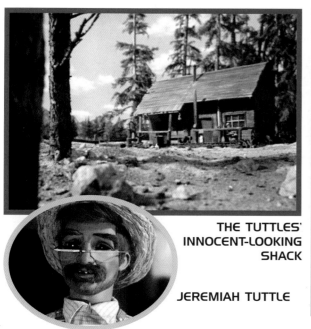

THE TUTTLES'
INNOCENT-LOOKING
SHACK

JEREMIAH TUTTLE

THE TUTTLES' SUPERCHARGED MODEL T

Challenge Set By: Brains

O h...er...hi there...This is Brains speaking. I gave my robot assistant Braman the task of reprogramming the blueprint storage files in my computer, but he must have forgotten to check the system for programming bugs, because all the print-outs are being scrambled. Can you redraw the contents of the print-out grid into the blank grid below to correct the error?

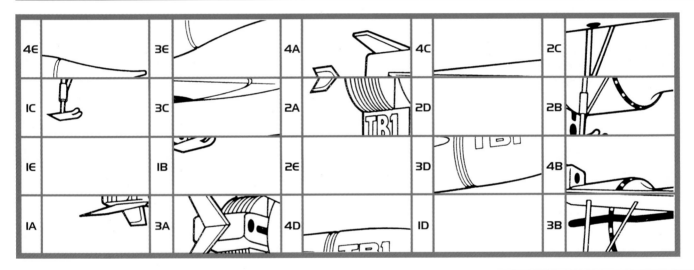

See page 60 for Solutions.

Challenge Set By: Parker

O h, 'ello...this is Parker speaking. So, 'ow well do you know your colleagues in h'International Rescue? That's the idea behind this little test, to see if you really know who's who and what's what about the Tracys, their friends and also their h'enemies.

If you need any clues, you might find them h'elsewhere in this 'ere dossier.

JEFF TRACY

1. Was Mr Tracy a member of:
A. The World Health Authority?
B. The World Space Agency?
C. The World Intelligence Network?

2. Is Mr Tracy's personal jet:
A. A Nitro-G?
B. A Thrust 1?
C. A Condor XL6?

ALAN TRACY

1. Is Alan's favourite pop group:
A. The Groovemovers?
B. The Cass Carnaby Five?
C. The Kings Road Swingers?

2. Alan recently won a Grand Prix. Was it at:
A. Parola Sands?
B. Brands Hill?
C. The Gotterdammering?

BRAINS

1. Brains has a robot called:
A. Roboman?
B. Electroman?
C. Braman?

2. Which of the following vehicles was not designed by Brains:
A. Skythrust?
B. Skydiver?
C. Skyship 1?

LADY PENELOPE

1. 'Er Ladyship's friend the Duchess of Royston has a portrait of a gazelle. Is it by:
A. Toulouse de Monet?
B. Vincent Verneer?
C. Braquasso?

2. A fabric was named after 'er Ladyship. Was it:
A. Penelon?
B. Skylon?
C. Fablon?

TIN-TIN

1. Tin-Tin and 'er Ladyship have a favourite fashion designer. Is it:
A. Rudi Gaudi?
B. Ginani Martini?
C. François Lemaire?

2. Tin-Tin's favourite DJ is:
A. Pete Pringle?
B. Rick O'Shay?
C. Jimmy Rushes?

PARKER

1. My favourite food is:
A. Fish and chips?
B. Spaghetti?
C. Stew?

2. My nickname is:
A. Fingers?
B. Nosey?
C. Cloth Ears?

THE HOOD

1. Is this right villain's base:
A. A Far Eastern temple?
B. Joe's Kozy Korner Kafe?
C. The back of a lorry?

2. He uses a company for a cover. Is it:
A. The North Pole Laundry?
B. The Sweepomatic Brush Company?
C. Arkan Double Glazing Limited?

See page 60 for Solutions.

Report Filed By: Parker

Now, 'er Ladyship 'as h'asked me to dish the dirt – er, I mean prepare an official report – on some of the dodgy geezers and right villains the h'International Rescue team has had the misfortune to come up against in the time they've been h'operating. Of course, they're all safely locked up now, but as my old mate Light Fingered Fred always used to say, "The real villains are the ones that 'aven't been nicked" – and 'e should know!

DR GODBER

Crimes: Kidnapping, blackmail, attempted murder

This bloke was a really nasty piece of work. I first clapped eyes on 'im in Paris, when 'e tried to put 'er Ladyship out of h'action with a drugged drink. After that failed, 'e then tried to gas 'er at the 'eraldic h'archives, and finally 'e tied 'er to a maintenance ladder in the h'Anderbad Tunnel, right in the path of the Anderbad Express. Luckily, h'International Rescue reached 'er first, but I don't like thinking about what nearly happened.

CHANDLER AND BROPHY

Crimes: Kidnapping, theft, extortion

Two scheming lowlifes who thought they could take advantage of a penniless h'old lady. But they shouldn't have picked on the Duchess of Royston! When the old dear was locked up in a fiery death trap, 'er Ladyship and I managed to lend an 'elping 'and, and the Thunderbirds boys were able to save 'er and 'er precious painting.

THE ERDMAN GANG

Crimes: Kidnapping, attempted murder, international sabotage

This bunch thought they were real clever. Their trick was to strap exploding bracelets to 'elpless people so as to force them to carry out acts of sabotage. Thanks to h'International Rescue, though, the world got wise to their devious dodge, and 'er Ladyship and I 'ad the very great pleasure of shooting them down in flames.

JENKINS AND CORELLA

Crimes: Theft, international espionage, criminal deception

This pair gave Mr Tracy and 'is boys a scare, and could 'ave put the world h'at risk when they stole military secrets. Using the good name of h'International Rescue, they pulled off a job so h'audacious that even I 'ad to h'admire it. But they 'adn't counted on our network of h'undercover agents, who made them spill the beans.

OLSEN

Crimes: International espionage, sabotage, attempted murder

It wasn't so much show business as snow business when this bloke led me and 'er Ladyship a merry dance through the Swiss h'Alps. I 'ad to risk life and limb to put a stop to 'is caper, but 'e soon found himself playing a different tune. I'm just glad I remembered to pack my parachute brolly!

REPORT FILED BY **JOHN TRACY**

"Hi there, John Tracy recording. Being responsible for Thunderbird 5 means I don't go out on as many rescues as my brothers, but from up here I can see just how important it is that International Rescue works as a team. Like the time a case of food poisoning almost created a major disaster."

LOCATION: SOUTH AMERICA.

HE'S ALMOST HERE.

BETTER SAY HELLO TO THE GUY.

THE NEW ARRIVAL: A GIANT NUCLEAR-POWERED MOBILE WOOD-PULPING PLANT.

BASE CONTROL TO CRABLOGGER 1. BETTER GET OUT YOUR TUXEDOS...I'M GOING TO SHOW YOU THE SIGHTS TONIGHT.

AND THAT EVENING...

HERE WE ARE, SEÑORES. THREE SPECIALS AND ONE STEAK.

SO WHILE VIRGIL LAUNCHED THUNDERBIRD 2...

LADY PENELOPE AND PARKER SET OUT ON THEIR MISSION.

BY NOW THE CRABLOGGER WAS APPROACHING THE VILLAGE OF SAN MARTINO.

JANSON HELD HIS BREATH.

IF THE CRABLOGGER GETS JAMMED WITH RUBBLE, THEY'LL HEAR THE BANG A HUNDRED MILES AWAY.

BUT THE CRABLOGGER PLOUGHED STRAIGHT THROUGH THE VILLAGE...

DESTROYING EVERYTHING IN ITS PATH.

NOW IT WAS HEADING STRAIGHT FOR THE SAN MARTINO DAM!

VIRGIL AND BRAINS WERE NOW TOUCHING DOWN AT BASE CONTROL...

TO UNLOAD THE MOBILE CRANE.

WITH SCOTT AT THE CONTROLS, THEY SOON CAUGHT UP WITH THE CRABLOGGER.

THERE IT IS!

RIGHT! YOU KNOW THE PLAN. GET TO YOUR POSITIONS.

AS SCOTT BROUGHT THE CRANE ALONGSIDE, HE OPERATED A CONTROL TO RAISE BRAINS AND VIRGIL TO THE ROOF OF THE CRABLOGGER –

WHERE VIRGIL BEGAN CUTTING THROUGH TO THE CONTROL CABIN.

HE AND BRAINS SOON REACHED THE TRAPPED CREW.

THEY DON'T LOOK TOO GOOD, SCOTT. THE SOONER WE GET THEM OUT OF HERE THE BETTER.

NOW ONLY LADY PENELOPE COULD STOP THE CRABLOGGER ON ITS JOURNEY OF DESTRUCTION.

UNTIL...

THANK YOU, MR LUCAS. YOU HAVE BEEN MOST COOPERATIVE.

AFTER WHICH THE CRABLOGGER SHOULD...STOP.

BEFORE SENDING LUCAS BACK TO SLEEP WITH HER TRANQUILLIZER PISTOL, LADY PENELOPE PASSED THE RECORDING TO PARKER...

WHO TRANSMITTED THE INSTRUCTIONS BY RADIO TO THUNDERBIRD 5...

WE'VE NOW PROGRAMMED THE HAND-CONTROL...

AND I RELAYED THEM VIA SATELLITE LINK...

AND IT IS NOW POSSIBLE TO BREAK THE INTERLOCK WHICH PREVIOUSLY HELD THE REMOTE-CONTROL LEVER IN POSITION...

TO VIRGIL AND BRAINS ABOARD THE CRABLOGGER.

TO CLOSE THE REACTOR DOWN COMPLETELY, YOU MUST DEPRESS THE BUTTON MARKED "CLOSING RELEASE". THE UNIT INCORPORATES A TIME-LAG OF ABOUT THREE MINUTES, AFTER WHICH THE CRABLOGGER SHOULD...STOP.

THREE MINUTES! WE'LL NEVER MAKE IT IN TIME!

WAS THE SAN MARTINO DAM DOOMED TO DESTRUCTION?

52

SLOWLY, THE CRABLOGGER BEGAN CLIMBING THE LEDGE ABOVE THE DAM SITE...

WITH BRAINS AND VIRGIL AS HELPLESS PASSENGERS...

WHILE SCOTT RACED TOWARDS THEM IN A SUPERON TANKER.

VIRGIL – YOU AND BRAINS WILL HAVE TO BE READY TO HOOK UP THE PIPELINES.

F.A.B., SCOTT.

BUT WOULD HE BE TOO LATE?

FINALLY, THE CRABLOGGER DREW TO A HALT.

TWO MINUTES TO GO!

SHE'S STOPPED!

I KNOW, SIMMS, BUT JUST THINK WHERE SHE'S STOPPED!

ONLY YARDS AWAY FROM THE DAM ON THE PRECARIOUSLY BALANCED CRABLOGGER, VIRGIL AND BRAINS ANXIOUSLY WAITED FOR SCOTT.

STAND BY TO HOOK UP THE PIPELINES.

BUT NOW THE GROUND WAS CRUMBLING BENEATH ITS WHEELS!

AT LAST SCOTT REACHED THE SCENE.

SUPERON

THE FUEL LINES WERE ATTACHED...

OK, SCOTT, START THE PUMPS!

AND SLOWLY THE HIGHLY EXPLOSIVE FUEL WAS DRAINED INTO THE TANKER.

FUEL
1000 GALLS
FULL

500 GALLONS TO GO...

CRABLOGGER TANK CAPACIT

UNTIL...

HECK! SHE'S GOING!

RIGHT, THAT'S IT. QUICK, BRAINS – JUMP!

BRAINS AND VIRGIL ACTIVATED THEIR JET-PACKS...

54

Agent Challenge: Wired for Danger

Challenge Set By: Scott Tracy

This is Scott Tracy reporting. The Hood has hacked into the Master Control of a manned rocket and activated the destruct program. If we don't clear this program from the system, the rocket will explode and cause untold harm. In order to carry out our mission we need to match the coloured wires from the Master Control to one of the four Auxiliary Panels. The colours of only one panel match up. See if you can trace the wiring to find which one it is.

THE HOOD

MANNED ROCKET

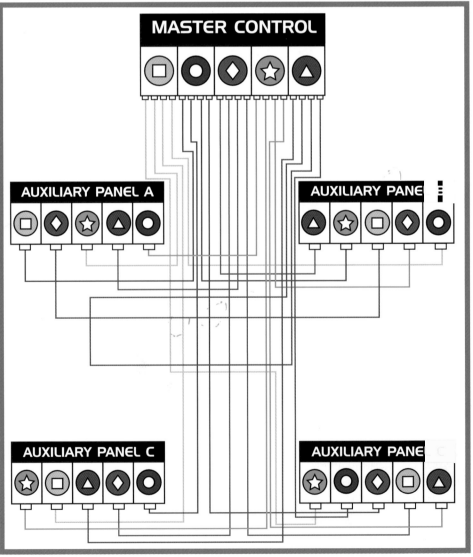

See page 60 for Solutions.

Agent Challenge: Wish You Were...Where?

Challenge Set By: Lady Penelope

This is Lady Penelope calling...Jeff Tracy has sent me to find four international villians who are hiding out in four different European locations. I need to tell Jeff where they are, but my transmission frequency is being monitored by the enemy state of Bereznik. I've decided to use postcards to let him know where I've found each villian. If you look at the postcard I sent from Paris, you'll see that each letter of the villian's name appears in the correct order within my message. Where did I find the three other villians?

I've dared Parker to go paragliding, but he's reluctant!

MONTE BIANCO

Villains

Dr Godber
Mr Steelman,
Colonel Tobolsk.

Sailed into Monte Carlo yesterday with Parker at the helm and dropped anchor!

MONTE CARLO

PARIS

It's cold on the slopes, but I've been tobogganing and downhill-skiing!

PARADISE PEAKS

Do wish <u>th</u>at Virgil was h<u>e</u>re – h<u>e</u>'d ad<u>o</u>re the m<u>o</u>dern art!

The Hood

See page 60 for Solutions

57

Challenge Set By: John Tracy

Hi there! This is John Tracy speaking. Freak weather in the Pacific has created static interference that has affected our reception of images of Thunderbird 5, and some visual records are now permanently corrupted.

Can you closely examine the two pictures below, identify how they are different and confirm which one is the true likeness, A or B?

ACCORDING TO BRAINS, THERE ARE II DIFFERENCES. CAN YOU FIND THEM ALL?

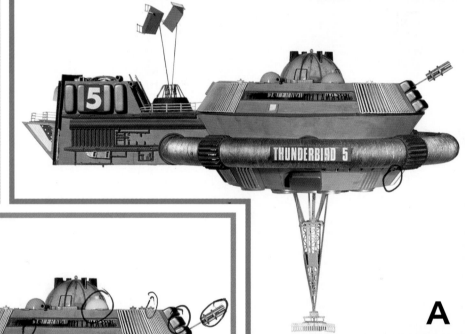

A

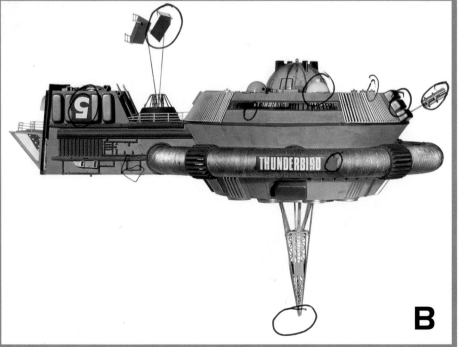

B

WHEN YOU KNOW WHAT THEY ARE, CIRCLE THE DIFFERENCES ON THE WRONG IMAGE.

See page 60 for Solutions

Challenge Set By: Jeff Tracy

Hi there! This is Jeff Tracy speaking. Would you like to be one of our agents? You need to be a very special sort of person to understand how International Rescue works. Often we have to use codes to avoid letting our enemies know what we are doing. Here's a simple code for you to try and crack. To help you start, we have provided boxes for you to finish filling in. Then see if you can read the message I am planning to send.

20•8•21•14•4•5•18•2•9•18•4•19
1•18•5   7•15!

A	1	N	14	
B	2	O	15	
C	3	P	16	
D	4	Q	17	
E	5	R	18	
F	6	S	19	
G	7	T	20	
H	8	U	21	
I	9	V	22	
J	10	W	23	
K	11	X	24	
L	12	Y	25	
M	13	Z	26	

Write your message here:

Thunderbirds ARE

Go !

See page 60 for Solutions

Sun-spot Alert
pg22

Signals 1 and A combined read:
"This is Control Tower. Aircraft crash-landed on roof. Passengers trapped."

Signals 2 and B combined read:
"This is car two one calling Spoke City control. No incidents to report at present."

Signals 3 and C combined read:
"This is Desert Survey Team Seven. Have now completed work in this area as planned."

Signals 1 and A combined are a distress call.

Countdown to Disaster
pg23

The rocket has crashed closest to Vehicle A, Thunderbird 2.

The Scramblebug
pg40

Personal Inquiries
pg41

Jeff Tracy:	1B, 2C	Alan Tracy:	1B, 2A
Brains:	1C, 2B	Penelope:	1C, 2A
Tin-Tin:	1C, 2B	Parker:	1C, 2B
The Hood:	1A (and sometimes 1C), 2A		

Wired for Danger
pg56

Auxiliary Panel C has the matching coloured wires.

Wish You Were...Where?
pg57

Monte Carlo: Mr Steelman
Sailed into Monte Carlo yesterday with Parker at the helm and dropped anchor!

Paradise Peaks: Colonel Tobolsk
It's cold on the slopes, but I've been tobogganing and downhill-skiing!

Monte Bianco: Dr Godber
I've dared Parker to go paragliding, but he's reluctant!

Electric Storm
pg58

Picture A is the true likeness of Thunderbird 5. The yellow circles indicate where you will find the differences.

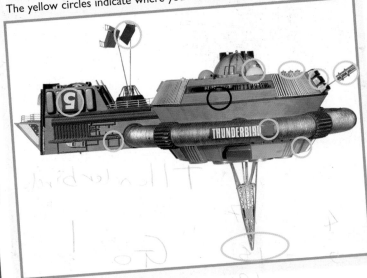

Code Crackers
pg59

The message should read:

THUNDERBIRDS ARE GO!

Well done, you're a credit to International Rescue!